The Naughty Newlywed Game

A Sexy Game of Questions for Couples

Do you know your partner's sexy secrets?

J.R. James

Copyright © 2020 Love & Desire Press

Written by J.R. James

All rights reserved.

ISBN 978-1-952328-45-9 (paperback)

Spice up your love life even more, and explore all the discussion books for couples by J.R. James:

Love and Relationship Books for Couples

Would You Rather...? The Romantic Conversation Game for Couples (Love and Romance Edition)

Sexy Game Books for Couples

Would You Rather...? The Naughty Conversation Game for Couples (Hot and Sexy Edition)

Truth or Dare? The Sexy Game of Naughty Choices (Hot and Wild Edition)

Never Have I Ever... An Exciting and Sexy Game for Adults (Hot and Dirty Edition)

The Hot or Not Quiz for Couples: The Sexy Game of Naughty Questions and Revealing Answers

Pillow Talk: The Sexy Game of Naughty Trivia Questions for Couples

The Naughty Newlywed Game: A Sexy Game of Questions for Couples

Sexy Discussion Books for Couples

Let's Talk Sexy: Essential Conversation Starters to Explore Your Lover's Secret Desires and Transform Your Sex Life

All **THREE** *Let's Talk About...* sexy question books in one massive volume for one low price. Save now!

Let's Talk About... Sexual Fantasies and Desires: Questions and Conversation Starters for Couples Exploring Their Sexual Interests

Let's Talk About... Non-Monogamy: Questions and Conversation Starters for Couples Exploring Open Relationships, Swinging, or Polyamory

Let's Talk About... Kinks and Fetishes: Questions and Conversation Starters for Couples Exploring Their Sexual Wild Side

Change your sex life forever through the power of sexy fun with your spouse, partner, or lover!

www.sexygamesforcouples.com

Sexy Vacations for Couples
https://geni.us/Passion

HOW TO PLAY THE GAME

The rules for this game are very simple, and is intended for any couple, married or otherwise.

Like the original *Newlywed Game*, you and your partner can test your knowledge of each other by trying to guess how your partner would answer a question. Unlike the original game, these questions are all about sexual fantasies, desires, intimate history, and everything sexy.

One player reads the question. The other player guesses how their partner would answer the question. Take turns going back and forth asking and answering the questions. Keep count of each player's number of correct answers.

At the end of each round, there will be a *"Sexy Reward"* page. Whichever player had the most correct answers in the round, wins a sexy reward from their partner. (In the event of a tie, both players get the reward!)

For example: Dennis and Kelly are playing together. It's Kelly's turn to be asked a question so Dennis reads, "What is my favorite sexual position?" Kelly knows Dennis likes when she is on top of him, so that's what she guesses his answer would be. Dennis agrees that's his favorite position, and Kelly gets a point. Dennis can then try and guess what Kelly's answer to that question would be to receive a point as well. Both players get a chance to win! After the last question of the round is answered, Dennis and Kelly would tally their points to see who wins the *Sexy Reward*. Once the reward is completed, start a new round.

As you spend time discussing the answers, you'll soon you'll find yourselves smiling, laughing, and enjoying the sexually charged conversation. Who knows? You may even discover new sexual possibilities for your relationship.

If your partner doesn't know all of your likes or desires, don't be upset! Now is the perfect time to help them learn your favorite ways to get down and dirty.

Just have fun, because as long as you're enjoying time with your partner and having sexy conversation, you both win!

ROUND

1

1
Where were we the first time we made out?

2
What kind of music, if any, do I prefer for sexy-time?

3
What area of my body do I like massaged?

4
Do I prefer to dominate or submit in bed?

5
What's one sexual thing I cannot live without ?

6
What's my favorite time of day for love making ?

7

Besides the bedroom, where else do I like to have sex?

_8_

Do I have a favorite pre -sex drink or cocktail ?

9
Would I rather give a lap dance or receive one?

10
What parts of my body do I like bitten or sucked?

Sexy Reward

The winner of this round gets a sultry lap dance to the song of their choice.

ROUND

2

11

What physical trait of mine am I most proud of?

12
Which do I find sexier: intelligence or a sense of humor?

13
What movies or TV shows can get me in the mood?

14
What's one food that I'd like to use during sex?

15
Do I enjoy being naked?

16
What's one of my sexual fantasies?

17
Do I consider myself a jealous person?

<u>18</u>
What's one kink or fetish I'd like to try?

19
*Which do I prefer:
oral or anal sex?*

20
*Would I be willing
to striptease if the
price was right ?*

Sexy Reward

The loser has to try and make the winner moan in pleasure within two minutes. You can do it in whatever way you think will work the quickest.

ROUND

3

21
Do I have a favorite sex toy?

22
Would I be willing to have a threesome?

23
What kind of clothing do I find sexy?

24
What's my favorite sexy song?

25
What are two things that turn me on?

<u>26</u>
What was an embarrassing sexual moment from my past ?

27
What do I like to do after sex?

28
What's one of my biggest turn -offs?

29

In general, am I more attracted to people taller or shorter than myself ?

30

What part of someone's body catches my attention first?

Sexy Reward

The winner of this round gets a sexy massage for three minutes.

ROUND

4

31
Do I like being tied up or handcuffed?

32
Who is one celebrity that turns me on?

33
What's the most sexually daring thing I've ever done?

34

Is there anything I don't like to do in bed?

35

What's one thing you do in bed that I love?

36

If I had to choose, would I rather have sex in front of a couple, or watch them having sex in front of me?

37
What makes me feel desired?

38
Where on my body am I ticklish?

39
What kind of vacation would I find erotic ?

40
How do I feel about having sex in a pool?

Sexy Reward

The loser of this round needs to softly tease the winner's chest, neck, and ears with their lips for one minute.

ROUND

5

41
Do I like to be vocal during sex?

42

If we were to roleplay, what role would I like to play?

43

Is there any part of my body that is "off-limits ?"

44

What kind of kissing do I enjoy the most?

45

Do I prefer the lights on or the lights off?

46

Where is one place I'd never have sex?

47
What is one profession I find super sexy?

48
What do I like to see you wearing for a sexy evening?

49

Would I prefer sex in the tub or in the shower?

50

Would I be willing to star in a porno if the price was right ?

Sexy Reward

The winner of this round gets to pick any part of their body and have the loser sensually and seductively shower kisses on it for two minutes.

ROUND

6

51
What's my idea of great foreplay?

52
Would I rather receive a sexy text message or a sexy photo?

53
Would I consider myself a sexual person?

54
Have I ever had sex in a vehicle?

55
What is my favorite thing about you?

56
What do I think makes for hotter sex, physical attraction or emotional connection?

57
What's my favorite "dirty" thing to say or hear?

58
How often do I masturbate ?

59
Am I turned on by sexting?

60

Would I play strip poker (or other strip game) in a group setting ?

Sexy Reward

The loser of this round needs to give the winner a foot massage for two minutes while listing off all the amazing things they do in bed. (If you don't know how they are in bed, then use your imagination.)

ROUND

7

61
What's my favorite sexual position ?

62

Are there any specific books or magazines that turn me on ?

63

Have I been to a nude beach (or would I be willing to go)?

64

Would I prefer to make a sex video or pose for a sexy photo shoot?

65

What's one word I'd use to describe our sex life?

66
Would I like to have sex outside? If so, where?

67
What's the funniest sexual experience I've ever had?

68
Do I like my hair pulled during sex?

69

Do I enjoy the 69 position?

70

How old was I the first time I had sex?

Sexy Reward

The loser has three minutes to try and make the winner smile using whatever means necessary. Be creative.

ROUND

8

71
Can you describe any details about my first kiss ?

72
Do I prefer to initiate sex, or have you do it?

73
What type of underwear do I like to wear?

74
Do I like to be spanked?

75
Do I prefer hair or clean-shaven?

76
Do I like a long session of sex or a passionate quickie?

77

How do I feel about BDSM?

78

Besides a bed or sofa, what's the next best piece of furniture I'd have sex on?

79
Are there any sexual positions I don't enjoy?

80
What is the most amount of times I've had sex in one day?

Sexy Reward

The loser has togently tease and pleasure the winner using only their hands and fingertips for three minutes.

ROUND

9

81

Have I ever had sex in an "inappropriate" setting or situation ?

82
How did I first learn about sex?

83
What kind of Halloween costume would I find sexy?

84
How long was the longest sexual session I've ever had?

85
What's one thing on my sexual "bucket list?"

86
How many people have I had sex with ?

87
How long did we wait before having sex?

88
Where did we go on first date ?

89

Is there a physical activity (other than sex) that turns me on?

90

What's one new thing I'd like to try in bed?

Sexy Reward

The loser has to tease the winner with their tongue for two minutes in whatever way they wish.

ROUND

10

91
Do I have any sexual regrets?

92
Would I consider myself "kinky" in the bedroom?

93
Where is the strangest place we've ever had sex?

94
*What would I say
I do best in bed?*

95
*What do I like to
wear when I feel
sexy?*

<u>96</u>
Describe a situation I might find erotic ?

97
Have I ever played dirty Truth or Dare in a group setting? (If not, would I?)

98
What turns me on more: flirting or foreplay?

99
Are there any uniforms I find sexy?

100
Would I be turned on watching someone else masturbate?

Sexy Reward

Including this round, identify which player lost the most rounds and which player won the most rounds for the entire game.

The player who lost the most rounds needs to make one sexual fantasy come true for their partner. Winner's choice!

What's it going to be?

Spice up your love life even more, and explore all the discussion books for couples by J.R. James:

Love and Relationship Books for Couples

Would You Rather...? The Romantic Conversation Game for Couples (Love and Romance Edition)

Sexy Game Books for Couples

Would You Rather...? The Naughty Conversation Game for Couples (Hot and Sexy Edition)

Truth or Dare? The Sexy Game of Naughty Choices (Hot and Wild Edition)

Never Have I Ever... An Exciting and Sexy Game for Adults (Hot and Dirty Edition)

The Hot or Not Quiz for Couples: The Sexy Game of Naughty Questions and Revealing Answers

Pillow Talk: The Sexy Game of Naughty Trivia Questions for Couples

The Naughty Newlywed Game: A Sexy Game of Questions for Couples

Sexy Discussion Books for Couples

Let's Talk Sexy: Essential Conversation Starters to Explore Your Lover's Secret Desires and Transform Your Sex Life

All **THREE** *Let's Talk About...* sexy question books in one massive volume for one low price. Save now!

Let's Talk About... Sexual Fantasies and Desires: Questions and Conversation Starters for Couples Exploring Their Sexual Interests

Let's Talk About... Non-Monogamy: Questions and Conversation Starters for Couples Exploring Open Relationships, Swinging, or Polyamory

Let's Talk About... Kinks and Fetishes: Questions and Conversation Starters for Couples Exploring Their Sexual Wild Side

Change your sex life forever through the power of sexy fun with your spouse, partner, or lover!

www.sexygamesforcouples.com

Sexy Vacations for Couples

https://geni.us/Passion
ABOUT THE AUTHOR

J.R. James is a best-selling author who has a passion for bringing couples closer together and recharging their sexual intimacy. Erotic discussion is a powerfully sexy thing, and his conversation starter books have helped many couples reach new and sexually exciting heights in their relationships!

Sexy conversation with your partner is a magical, bonding experience. Through these best-selling question books, couples can find an easy way to engage in open and honest sexual discussion with each other. The result is a relationship that is both erotically charged and sexually liberating.

Printed in the USA
CPSIA information can be obtained
at www.ICGtesting.com
LVHW052051291024
795102LV00016B/813

9 781952 328459